669.3
T r 2
c. 1

22604

Tracy, Edward B
The new world of
copper

Date Due

| | | | |
|---|---|---|---|
| FEB 2 | 1971 | | |
| FEB 2 | 1971 | | |
| MAR. 15 | DORR H 1 02 2 '79 | | |
| MONTAGUE | IG S 1 0 8 '84 | | |
| 4-22 D | | | |
| 10-27 W | | | |
| 3-6 G | | | |
| | | | |
| | | | |
| | | | |

The story of copper and copper alloys and
their importance commercially is traced
from primitive times to the present with
photographs illustrating the efficient mining,
smelting, refining, and manufacturing methods of today.

# THE NEW WORLD
# OF COPPER

*Books by* EDWARD B. TRACY

# THE
# NEW WORLD
# OF COPPER

By EDWARD B. TRACY

*Illustrated with photographs*

DODD, MEAD & COMPANY, NEW YORK

TO MY WIFE, FRANCES PITTARD TRACY

*Frontispiece:* This extra high voltage cable, made of miles of copper wire, is for underground installation by the Philadelphia Electric Company.

## ACKNOWLEDGMENTS

The author is deeply indebted to the following for helpful information: The Anaconda Company, American Telephone & Telegraph Company, Anaconda American Brass Company, Anaconda Wire and Cable Company, Copper Development Association, Inc., International Telephone and Telegraph Company, Southern New England Telephone Company, and United States Lines Company.

### PICTURE CREDITS

Anaconda American Brass Company, 36, 37, 39, 40, 41, 42, 44, 45, 46, 59, 77; The Anaconda Company, 16, 23, 27; Anaconda Wire and Cable Company, 2; Anaconda Wire and Cable Company and Inspiration Copper Company, 19; Andes Copper Mining Company, a subsidiary of The Anaconda Company, 21, 31; Baldwin-Lima-Hamilton Corporation, Eddystone Division, 60; The Boeing Company, 62; Copper Development Association, Inc., 6, 11, 58, 68, 70; General Electric Company, 65, 78; International Telephone and Telegraph Company, 54; Nacional De Cobre, S.A., 72, 76; United States Lines Company, 57; Western Electric Company, 51, 53.

# Contents

# 1 Copper–One of Man's Greatest Metals

Copper is one of man's most useful metals. The economy in many countries is measured by tons of steel, barrels of oil or the volume of electricity produced, but the progress that has been attained in connection with these products would not have been possible if it had not been for copper. Its uses as a pure metal in the form of sheets, strips, rods, wire, tubing, special shapes, or as a base for alloying with other metals, are almost endless.

As the best known commercial conductor of electricity, it has been in the past and continues to be a major factor in a long list of important electrical developments. It has an invaluable role in the conveying of electrical energy from the great power generating plants to the mills and factories that have made America and other countries advance so effectively as industrial nations. It has been the artery through which electricity has been carried into countless homes, to make life easier and pleasanter for so many people.

Copper was selected for the famous Statue of Liberty in New York Harbor. It is made of 300 pieces of sheet copper, weighing 25 tons.

7

Copper has made available such everyday necessities as the telephone, telegraph and electric lights, as well as the generation and conveying of electricity for the operation of a long list of home and business appliances. Copper tubes and fittings have made it possible for millions of private residences and thousands of hospitals, schools, apartments, hotels and other types of buildings to have the most efficient plumbing systems which have contributed so much to the health of mankind.

Copper works for us every day in numerous ways. It offers us strength, economy, formability. It may be soldered, brazed or welded. It resists corrosion and has machinability, forgeability, durability, as well as color and beauty.

One of the oldest copper utensils in the museums of the United States is a copper frying pan, over five thousand years old, at the University of Pennsylvania. The earliest copper roof on record was the one on the cathedral at Hildesheim, Germany, built in the year 1320 A.D. Copper protected this historic house of worship for 600 years, until it was demolished by bombing during World War II. One of the oldest roofs in the United States is that on Christ Church at Philadelphia. It was built in 1732, which means that for well over 230 years this copper has resisted the ravages of time—and it appears to be in condition to battle the elements for 230 years more. The copper for this roof came from somewhere in Europe.

The enduring quality of copper was recently illustrated by a news item concerning the salvaging of a naval vessel which was damaged by gunfire during the Civil War and sank in the Mississippi River, near Vicksburg, Mississippi.

The salvage crew that is endeavoring to raise the ship has been warned of a possible hazard from explosives stored in containers that have been under water and mud for one hundred years. These containers were not made of steel or aluminum—they were made of COPPER.

8

# 2 The History of Copper

With the possible exception of gold, no other metal has had a more romantic history than copper. It was the first metal used by the human race. That was over four thousand years before iron came into use. It was the metal of the ancients, yet it is as modern as tomorrow.

Thousands of years ago, copper-bearing ores, like those containing other metals and minerals, were molten masses, deep in the fiery rocks.

During that period, tremendous pressures generated by volcanic and other disturbances caused the hot earth to flow, twist and heave, resulting in great cracks and depressions in the earth's crust. This continual twisting forced solutions containing copper and other metals into these cracks and crevices, where they were trapped.

As the earth cooled, these metals solidified, forming veins in hard rock or sulphide ores in the form of powdered earth. Although copper is a metal in itself, it occurs in combination with other metals, along with a large percentage of worthless rock.

The useless material is separated, other metals of value are recovered, and the copper content is carried through various complicated stages to the point of refined metal by processes which will be described later.

Copper is believed to have been discovered by primitive man during the earliest periods of civilization near the sites of the villages in the valleys of the Tigris and Euphrates Rivers, in what is now Iraq. This was about 800 B.C.

Copper deposits were worked in Egypt as early as 5000 B.C. Years later, copper was discovered and mined in substantial quantities on the Island of Cyprus, in the eastern area of the Mediterranean, close to Greece. The word "copper" comes from the name CYPRUS. The Romans called the red metal "aes cuprum," and finally it became known as copper, with the chemical or metallurgical symbol $cu$.

The struggle to obtain possession of the early copper mines led to numerous wars. Cyprus later passed to Phoenicia, then to Greece and on to Persia, now Iran, and then to Rome. Egypt, too, lost her mines to Assyria but, before this occurred, the Egyptians had made marked progress in the metallurgical field by learning how to combine copper with tin, thereby creating what for years was known as bronze. According to authorities, this was around 3800 B.C.

For a long time the term "commercial bronze" has been applied to an alloy of 90 per cent copper and 10 per cent zinc, but a true bronze contains copper and tin in varying amounts. However, there are many types of bronzes, phosphor bronze, manganese bronze, cadmium bronze and several others, all of which have a copper content of well over 80 per cent.

The Egyptians developed clever and ingenious craftsmen working with copper and some of the specimens of their efforts that may be seen today in museums attest to their remarkable skill.

As far as we know, the Egyptians were the first to make copper tubes and the best proof that they led the way in copper plumbing is shown in the accompanying photograph

10

Copper drainage pipe for bathing pool of Egyptian Pharaoh, Cheops, was found in usable condition more than 5,000 years later.

of the copper pipe, still in good condition, that conveyed water to the pyramid of Cheops, Egyptian Pharaoh, over five thousand years ago.

In 1240 B.C., the enterprising Phoenicians started work at the famous Rio Tinto copper deposits in Spain.

In North America, in 1609, the explorer, Henry Hudson, discovered that the Indians in the Lake Superior region had necklaces fashioned of a red metal. Some also had metal arrowheads, axes and knives which had been hammered out of copper that evidently was unusually pure.

The first copper deposit in the United States that was really worked was the Simsbury mine, at Granby, Connecticut. According to records, it was discovered in 1705 and mining operations continued there until 1770. It was not a profitable venture and during this entire period the amount of copper produced was very small measured by today's standards.

Later, the northern peninsula of Michigan became a major producer.

Many years ago, the Indians of Peru discovered copper high in the Andes Mountains of South America. They melted and fashioned it into implements and ornaments. Today, some of the same deposits are being worked at an elevation close to 13,000 feet, on the property of Cerro Corporation. The railroad at one point in this area, is almost 16,000 feet, the world's highest. Within the last few years, four North American mining companies have combined to develop and operate a large deposit of copper ore in Southern Peru.

Several hundred years ago, far to the southward, in the Chilean Andes, primitive Indians, and later the Spaniards, knew of copper deposits and worked them.

Today, in the world famous Chuquicamata mine, in the Chilean Andes, 10,000 feet above sea level, engineers and miners of the Anaconda Company are taking out thousands of tons of copper-bearing ore every day. This is what is known as an open pit operation, carried on in an enormous man-made depression or hollow. It is the largest known deposit of copper in the world.

The average copper content of the ore in this mine is 1.86 per cent. This means that from every short ton (2000 pounds) of rock and soil 37.2 pounds of usable copper are recovered.

While the average copper content of ore in Chile is approximately 2 per cent and the African ores range from 3 per cent to 6 per cent, the average among the mines in the United States is only nine-tenths of 1 per cent or 18 pounds of copper recovered for every ton of rock or earth handled.

12

Copper-bearing ores have been found in almost every country of the world and in half of the states of the United States, but the deposits in many of the latter areas have not been of sufficient size to warrant the cost of operation.

Today, in North America, 95 per cent of the known worthwhile copper deposits are concentrated in the Rocky Mountain region, in Arizona, Utah, Montana, New Mexico and Nevada. Outside of these, Michigan is the largest producer.

As to the major sources throughout the world, four-fifths of the supply of new copper comes from nine countries—the United States, Chile, Peru, Northern Rhodesia, Canada, the Belgian Congo or Katanga, Spain, Mexico, and Kazakstan, in Southern Russia.

The following is a tabulation of the copper production in short tons (2000 pounds) during 1961 of the countries listed:

| Country | Tons Produced |
|---|---|
| United States | 1,159,556 |
| Northern Rhodesia | 633,534 |
| Chile | 603,629 |
| Russia (estimated at) | 550,000 |
| Canada | 449,791 |
| Congo | 324,422 |
| Japan | 106,317 |
| Republic of South Africa | 55,464 |
| Mexico | 54,359 |
| Total | 3,937,072 |

During the year 1962, the copper mines of the free world produced 4,415,858 short tons of copper. Of this, the United States accounted for over 25 per cent, with Africa second, Chile third and Canada fourth.

Figures show that world consumption of copper has expanded at the rate of more than 3 per cent each year for many years and there is every indication that it will continue to grow at this rate—or even faster—in the future.

# 3 Locating Copper Deposits

Bingham Canyon, the great copper deposit in Utah, was discovered as the result of a Sunday picnic. The Mormons and the Forty-niners, the latter on their way to seek gold in California, passed over some rich and extensive copper deposits without being aware of it.

The discovery at Bingham came about in this way. After the Mormons were settled at Salt Lake they needed protection from the Indians. The Government dispatched a platoon of troops from Fort Douglas to safeguard the Mormon settlement. This was during the summer of 1862. Soon after the soldiers arrived, the officer in charge gave a picnic in Bingham Canyon. One of the ladies in the group picked up a shining stone that was found to be rich copper ore. This was the first indication that copper-bearing ore was in this area. Later, after exploration and development, it proved to be one of the richest copper deposits in the world.

There is a copper mine on one of the islands of the West Indies that has been in production for forty years. It was discovered by a medical doctor whose mule or horse tore a shoe loose while the physician was riding across a mountain trail to a remote village. He used a rock about the size of a person's fist to hammer the nails and fasten the shoe back in place. The rock broke in half, revealing veins of some sort of metal. Not being a geologist, the doctor did not know what the mineral was. He took the samples along with him and, sometime later, a mining engineer pronounced it to be high grade copper-bearing ore. There have been years when this mine, discovered by sheer chance, produced 20,000 tons of the red metal.

Mines are where man discovers the mineral deposit. A manufacturing plant can be built almost anywhere one wants to locate it, with careful consideration of the market, the availability of labor, power, water, etc. But mines are located only where the earth's riches have been placed.

When Stanley made his first historic journey across Africa in search of Dr. Livingstone, in 1871, he found some of the chiefs of savage tribes and their wives wearing copper rings, necklaces and leg bands. They also had certain other copper articles and utensils. Stanley was the first person to recognize the mineral wealth of the Congo. But it was not until years later, after the investment of millions—which included the building of a railroad well over a thousand miles long, and a constant struggle against malaria, black-water fever, torrential rains, the dreaded tsetse fly, and hostile natives—that the Katanga mines came into production on a large and profitable scale.

South of Katanga, between the Congo and Zambesi Rivers, is the boundary between Katanga territory and the British Crown Colony of Northern Rhodesia. Geologists found that the same rock formation existed on both sides of the border—so why shouldn't there be copper in the Rhodesian area as well as in Katanga, they reasoned.

It was about 1925 when one of the large companies sent William C. Collier, an engineer born in Dorchester, England,

Open pit operations at the Berkeley Mine at Butte, Montana, with a production of eighty million pounds of copper annually

to explore the area. In the vast wilderness near the famous Victoria Falls he and his group of natives encountered an old medicine man of the Bantu Tribe with ornaments of malachite ore. Collier knew that malachite was very rich copper ore and he bribed the native witch doctor to tell him where it had come from. Collier followed his directions and, late one afternoon, the engineer and his Rhodesian natives came to a clearing at a bend of a river. Across the clearing, an antelope was grazing. This meant meat for the engineer's bearers. After he had shot it, he went ahead to examine it. When the animal had fallen it had disturbed some earth with a hoof or a horn, revealing a chunk of malachite ore rich in copper.

Later, Collier discovered pits where natives had dug out

16

ore. Here he staked a claim and named it the Roan-Antelope claim. The MacLaren shaft, the deepest at the Roan-Antelope mine, was down to 4,054 feet as of September 1963.

Next to those in the United States and Chile, the copper mines of Northern Rhodesia have been the third largest producing area in the world.

While some copper deposits have been found by chance, with little if any effort and expense, others have been discovered by prospectors who, with either a horse, mule or donkey to carry supplies, have spent lonely days, weeks and years roaming the deserts, mountains and valleys in search of an outcropping that would reveal the presence of a mineral where they might stake a claim.

Most of the producing copper mines in Latin America were known by the Spaniards. During comparatively recent years, great developments have taken place in the invention and use of scientific equipment to be used in the discovery of metal deposits. Several copper ore bodies of substantial proportions have been located by flying over mineralized areas, using delicate and expensive instruments to detect the metal's presence. The real work begins after discovery, however, with an enormous investment in engineering talent, equipment, construction and labor.

Even though the United States and various other sections of the world have been well prospected and surveyed for copper—and other minerals of value—there is always the possibility there may be something just under the surface, waiting to be discovered. So be on the lookout, and should you find a stone that is fairly light green where the color appears to extend beyond the surface, it could be malachite. If it has a purplish cast and is much heavier than an ordinary rock, it could be bornite, which also has a high copper content. Should it have the appearance of containing gold, there is a possibility it could be another high grade copper ore—chalcopyrite.

17

# 4 Copper Ores

There are two types of copper-bearing ores—sulphide and oxide.

## Sulphide Ores

Sulphide ores are composed of copper-bearing sulphide minerals and are referred to as gangue. Gangue may be made up of useless minerals in addition to the copper or it may consist of several other worth-while minerals. It, also, may be formed of a combination of these two groups. The most important ores in this category are bornite, chalcopyrite, enargite, tetrahedrite, tennantite, chalcocite and covellite.

It is believed that approximately one half of the world's copper resources are in the form of chalcopyrite. Such ore is composed of sulphur, iron and copper.

## Oxidized Ores

In the oxidized group the ores have been mixed naturally just as the sulphide ores are, except that the gangue or rock and other minerals surrounding the copper have been altered by oxidation or weathering. Such copper-bearing ores are cuprite, tentorite, malachite, azurite, antlerite, brochantite and atacamite. The most common of these are malachite and azurite.

Loading copper ore at the open pit mine of Inspiration Copper Company in Arizona. A copper cable supplies power to the huge shovel.

# 5 Mines, Mining and the Treatment of Ores

One of the most unusual copper mines in existence is the famous El Salvador Mine, inside a mountain in Northern Chile, where 24,000 tons of copper-bearing ore are being taken out every day through a two-mile tunnel.

It is estimated that there are 375 million tons of ore in this deposit, with an average copper content of 1½ per cent. This means that thirty pounds of copper are recovered for every 2000 pounds of ore handled.

El Salvador, meaning "Savior" in Spanish, is one of the Chilean operations of Andes Copper Mining Company, a subsidiary of the Anaconda Company.

In order to mine this deposit successfully, it was necessary to tunnel through solid rock into the heart of Indio Muerto Mountain for a distance of two miles. Deep inside, miners drill and cut out great blocks of ore that break into small pieces by their own weight when they fall.

Trains haul the ore through the tunnel to a plant outside, where powerful equipment crushes and grinds the ore to nearly the fineness of flour. The next operation is "flotation."

20

The "El Salvador" Mine is in the India-Muerto Mountain in Chile. In the foreground is the new concentration plant.

This will be described in detail later. At this stage, the finely powdered copper concentrate is mixed with water and the solution or "slurry" is then transported fourteen miles, through a pipeline, to railroad yards. There the mixture is screened to get rid of the water. The powdered metal next is conveyed by train or trucks to the smelter, then on to the refinery, where it is made commercially pure, cast into various shapes and shipped to the markets of the world.

Transporting powdered ore in water by pipeline, in the way that it is done here, is one of the latest scientific developments, and the El Salvador operation has the distinction of being a pioneer in this method. The procedure may be copied at other mines in the future but, as of now, this is the first and only installation of its kind.

Some copper mines in Chile, Peru, Mexico, Africa and the United States are surface mines or open pit operations but there are many that are underground.

One of the deepest copper mines is the Mountain Con shaft of one of the Anaconda Company's properties at Butte, Montana, where copper bearing ore is being mined at a depth of over 5,296 feet. It is a great tribute to the engineering and metallurgical genius of the men conducting this operation that ores with the low copper content of those found here can be profitably handled from deposits at such a depth.

The first copper deposits at Butte, which for years have been yielding thousands of tons of the red metal a year, were discovered by men who were searching for gold and silver. Eager for precious metals, they regarded copper as a nuisance. This was about 1865, when the only plant for the treatment of copper ores was in Baltimore, Maryland. There were several facilities for reclaiming gold and silver but they were useless for handling copper-bearing ores. As the equipment at the Baltimore refinery was limited, some of the mine owners at Butte sent their ore to a smelter and refinery at Swansea, in Wales, for treatment. This took months and was costly. In 1867, a smelter was built in Butte, to treat gold, silver and copper ores. It was a crude affair but, with the discovery of more copper deposits and the increase in the use of the enduring metal, more smelters and refineries came into being with improved methods of operation. This was also the case with the mining and refining procedures.

Since that time, which was almost one hundred years ago, there have been radical changes in the operation of mines and refineries. A long list of men—laborers, mining engineers, chemists and metallurgists—in various countries have played an important part in developing methods to the high degree of perfection that they have achieved today.

Although copper is a basic metal, it must be pure—in most instances 99.95 per cent pure—before it is usable by the brass and copper mills and wire and cable plants. To accomplish this, the copper must first be separated from the useless mother rock or earth that surrounds it when it is mined. Then other metals, such as gold or silver, which are often found combined with the copper, are recovered, first by crushing the ore into fine particles—then by subjecting it to chemical treatment. Next it is smelted and finally refined.

Here are the main steps in the production of copper.

## Mining

There are two methods of mining copper; by open pit operation and by underground mining. There are two forms of the latter—vein mining and block caving.

## Open Pit Mining

As the name implies, this is an operation that is carried on in the open. It requires a great deal of heavy-duty, earth-moving equipment, many miles of railroad tracks and truck roads. At some of the large open pit mines it has been neces-

A full-revolving electric shovel in operation in an open pit mine. The men standing on the first level above the bucket give some idea of the enormous size of this piece of equipment.

sary to remove thousands of tons of earth and rock, referred to as over-burden, in order to reach the ore body. Quantities of explosives are required at some locations, to free waste rock which must be removed from the pits. As work progresses in an operation of this type, the hole that has been blasted and gouged out takes on the appearance of a huge amphitheater.

## Underground Mining

This method involves even more expense than open pit mining and a high grade ore is necessary in order to operate such a mine profitably.

A large underground copper mine is a very complicated and complex structure, with miles of electric railway tracks, lighting and ventilating systems, safety and fire-fighting devices, and telephone equipment in constant readiness for use. It is honeycombed with shafts and areas which have been drilled or blasted out of the ore-bearing rock, running horizontally from the vertical shafts, which are known as drifts.

The copper-bearing ore is drilled and dynamited deep underground, then transported by electrically operated mine cars to the shafts where it is brought to the surface in lifts and sent on to the next operation—that of milling.

## Block Caving

This form of underground mining has only been in use for a few years. It is employed where copper bearing ore is fairly well concentrated, but not necessarily high grade ore. Briefly, the operation consists of undercutting, by blasting, great masses of solid rock-bearing ore, which crumbles and falls of its own weight through control chutes, to be moved later by mine cars to the lifts that bring the ore to the surface. From there it goes to the crushers or milling operation.

Block caving, together with other improved smelting and refining methods, has made it possible to mine an enormous tonnage of ore which, at one time, was considered too low grade to handle profitably.

## Milling

The first step after ore is taken from the mine is to dump the large chunks into vast and powerful machines which break them into pieces six to eight inches in diameter. These pieces are again reduced in size—to not more than one inch in diameter—by smaller crushers.

## Screening

After milling, the ore is run onto vibrating screens which sift out all the pieces that are fine enough for wet grinding. Those pieces which are too large to go through the screens are fed into a third crusher and rescreened.

## Wet Grinding

The large chunks have now been broken into fragments but they are still too large. To further reduce the particles of ore, they are mixed with water and transferred to the wet grinding machines. This equipment consists of a heavy revolving cylinder partly filled with tons of manganese steel balls three or four inches in diameter. As the cylinder revolves, the action of the tumbling balls grinds the moist ore to powder.

## Classification

The finely ground mixture of water and ore is next automatically discharged into the pool of a classifier which is a rather shallow steel tank with a sloping bottom. By means of mechanical paddling, the water is constantly agitated. The largest particles of ore settle to the bottom. From here, they are carried up the slope by the action of a submerged rotating spiral cylinder and conveyed into the feedbox of another grinder or ball mill for further wet grinding. During this operation the ore that has been ground the finest overflows into another tank.

## Rough Flotation

These finely ground particles, which are referred to as "pulp" when mixed with water, are conveyed to a series of flotation machines. It is this process which first separates the copper from all other metals. A flotation machine consists of a tank equipped with an agitating mechanism. The pulp passes from one tank to another, where very carefully regulated amounts of chemicals, usually potassium zanthate and pine oil, have been added to the water. These chemicals create a froth which coats the copper minerals, causing them to adhere to the bubbles and float off on the top of the solution, to be further treated, while the useless rock particles sink to the bottom of the tank.

## Cleaner Flotation

The mineralized froth is passed on to a group of cleaner flotation tanks and then to recleaner tanks. During this procedure, still more water is added to dilute the froth. This causes the waste material to settle into the "cleaner tailings," which are pumped back into the rough flotation tanks in order to reclaim any particles of copper remaining. At this point, the thick waste is diverted and flows to the dumps.

## Concentrate Thickening

The product that now comes from the tanks is rich in copper concentrate, but it is mixed with a considerable amount of water. To reduce the water content, the metal particles are fed into what is known as a mechanical thickener where the solids settle to the bottom in the form of a heavy sludge.

## Filtering

The sludge is then conveyed to a vacuum filter, where all except 10 or 12 per cent of the water is removed by filtering. The remaining metal is called filter cake. From this process it goes to the storage beds, ready for the next operation, that of roasting.

One of the huge convertors at the Anaconda Company refinery in Montana

## Roasting

The concentrated filter cake, which often contains gold, silver, zinc, bismuth, antimony, arsenic, iron pyrite and sulphur, is subjected to a roasting operation before smelting. The main purpose of this step is to eliminate the sulphur. Roasting is done in what are known as multiple hearth furnaces, at a temperature of approximately 1350 degrees Fahrenheit.

## Smelting

The roasted metal then goes to reverberatory furnaces, where the temperature rises to well over 2500 degrees Fahrenheit. The metal melts and the heavier iron and copper sulphides settle to the bottom in an impure mixture called "matte."

## Converting

Next comes the final step in converting the ore to copper in metallic form. Cranes, capable of lifting hundreds of tons, convey the molten matte to a large converter. Slag, in the form of silica, is added to the molten metal. Then strong blasts of air are blown through the fiery mass by means of tubes in the sides of the converter, to eliminate injurious gasses. At various intervals, the worthless slag is drawn off and more matte added. Copper resulting from this operation is approximately 98 per cent pure.

## Refining

To conform to the present-day requirements of the modern brass and copper mills and the wire and cable plants, copper must be of a very high degree of purity, 99.90 per cent pure. Copper from the converters with a purity of 98 per cent is cast into shapes called "anodes." These are shipped to the electrolytic refinery for final purification.

## Electrolytic Refining

The copper anodes are suspended between thin plates of copper, referred to as "starting sheets." These sheets are submerged in long tanks that contain a solution of copper sulphate and sulphuric acid, known as an electric bath. As the result of the action of electrical currents passing through the bath, copper is dissolved from the heavy anodes and deposited on the cathodes or thin sheets.

This operation of consuming an anode usually requires twenty-six to twenty-eight days. It takes fourteen to fifteen days to produce a finished cathode, which is commercially pure copper, ready for the brass and copper mills.

## Fire Refining

Considerable copper is produced by fire refining. Blister copper is melted in huge furnaces where compressed air is forced through the pools of molten metal for the purpose of eliminating some of the impurities. The liquid metal is finally covered with a layer of coke and the end of a log of green wood is thrust into the molten mass, which has the effect of releasing some of the gasses. No one has yet found a better substitute for accomplishing the elimination of gasses.

The product resulting from fire refining is called tough-pitch of normal purity or tough-pitch of high conductivity if produced from the better quality blister or from some of the native Lake Superior copper.

# 6 Classification of Copper

These are the different grades of copper sold by producers.

LAKE—This is copper from the native copper mines of the Lake Superior region, with a minimum purity of 99.90 per cent, including the silver content.

ELECTROLYTIC—Copper that has been refined by the electrolytic process so it has a minimum copper content of 99.90 per cent, including silver.

FIRE REFINED—Copper plus silver, with a minimum copper content of 99.88 per cent.

CASTING—This copper, which usually is 99.50 per cent to 99.75 per cent pure, is made from scrap and is used for casting where no further reworking, such as rolling, drawing or forming is required.

BEST SELECTED—This grade averages 99.75 per cent and is used in the British brass trade.

TOUGH or TOUGH-PITCH—This again is a British copper of approximately 99.25 per cent purity.

CHILE BARS—Copper smelted in Chile, containing 95 per cent to 99 per cent copper and, in some instances, small amounts of silver and gold.

STANDARD—Copper which has either been electrically refined or fire-refined, averaging 99.70 per cent pure.

Matte—An intermediate product between copper-bearing ore and commercially pure copper that usually runs from 25 per cent to 55 per cent copper.

OFHC or oxygen-free high conductivity copper—A special type of copper, produced by melting and pouring copper in the presence of carbon, so that the metal does not absorb any oxygen. OFHC copper is used where exceptionally high conductivity, weldability and toughness are required for severe forming operations. It is used widely for many electrical and electronic applications.

Underground at the "El Salvador" Copper Mine of the Andes Copper Mining Company, Chile

# 7 Copper in Refinery Shapes

These are the different forms of refinery shapes used by brass mills, wire and cable plants and foundries.

Wire bars—Are about 3 to 4 inches square and 3 to 5 feet long. A common size weighs 250 pounds.

Ingots—Average weight 18 to 25 pounds, used for casting.

Cakes—Are supplied in the shape of squares or wedges, ranging from 2½ to 5¾ inches thick. Weight 140 to 4000 pounds.

Ingot bars—Also used for casting where larger shapes are required. Weights vary from 55 to 150 pounds.

Anodes—Usually 2 by 3 feet by 1½ inches thick, weighing approximately 250 pounds. This would be crude copper used by electrolytic refiners.

Cathodes—This is refined copper from electrolytic tanks in sheets 1 by 3 feet.

Billets—Diameters range from 3 to 12 inches, length from 15 to 50 inches. Weights range from 100 to 1500 pounds.

# 8 Ever-increasing Copper Alloys

Copper has been called "the friendly metal." It is as co-operative as it is useful. It can be mixed or alloyed with almost any metal, either nonferrous (meaning one not containing iron) or ferrous (meaning one with an iron content).

The result is that there are several hundred alloys where copper forms the basic content.

Copper and its alloys can either be cast, rolled, drawn, extruded, forged, swaged, spun or stamped into thousands of partly finished or finished items. It can also be welded, brazed, soldered and plated.

## Some Standard Alloys Where Copper Is the Base Metal

The following compositions are approximate.

| Name | Copper | Zinc | Lead | Tin | Manganese | Iron |
|---|---|---|---|---|---|---|
| Gilding | 95 | 5 | | | | |
| Commercial Bronze | 90 | 10 | | | | |
| Red Brass | 85 | 15 | | | | |
| Low Brass | 80 | 20 | | | | |

| Name | Copper | Zinc | Lead | Tin | Manganese | Iron |
|---|---|---|---|---|---|---|
| Cartridge Brass | 70 | 30 | | | | |
| Yellow Brass | 66 | 34 | | | | |
| Muntz Metal | 60 | 40 | | | | |
| Free Cutting Brass | 62 | 35 | 3 | | | |
| Hardware Bronze | 85 | 13.25 | 1.75 | | | |
| Admiralty | 70 | 29 | | 1 | | |
| Manganese Bronze | 59 | 39 | | .70 | .50 | .80 |
| Phosphor Bronze | 95 | | | 5 | | |

| Name | Copper | Zinc | Aluminum | Silicon | Nickel | Manganese |
|---|---|---|---|---|---|---|
| Aluminum Bronze | 95 | | 5 | | | |
| Silicon Bronze | 95.80 | | | 3.10 | | 1.10 |
| Nickel Silver 18% | 65 | 17 | | | 18 | |
| Cupro Nickel 10% | 90 | | | | 10 | |
| Cupro Nickel 30% | 70 | | | | 30 | |

## Some of the Metals That Have Been Alloyed with Copper

| Metal | Chemical Symbol | Melting Point Centigrade | Melting Point Fahrenheit | Electrical Conductivity | Year of Discovery | Discoverer |
|---|---|---|---|---|---|---|
| Copper | Cu | 1083 | 1981.4 | 100 | Pre-Historic | |
| Zinc | Zn | 419.46 | 787.03 | 29.1 | 1746 | Marggraf |
| Tin | Sn | 231.9 | 449.4 | 15 | Pre-Historic | |
| Nickel | Ni | 1455 | 2651 | 25.2 | 1751 | Cronstedt |
| Silicon | Si | 1430 | 2605 | | 1824 | Berzelius |
| Manganese | Mn | 1245 | 2273 | 0.9 | 1774 | Gahn |
| Lead | Pb | 327.4 | 621.3 | 8.3 | Pre-Historic | |
| Chromium | Cr | 1890 | 34.30 | 13.3 | 1798 | Vauquelin |
| Beryllium | Be | 1280 | 2340 | 29.2 | 1798 | Vauquelin |
| Aluminum | Al | 660.2 | 1220.4 | 64.9 | 1827 | Wohler |
| Cadmium | Cd | 320.9 | 609.6 | 25.2 | 1817 | Stromeyer |
| Phosphorus | P | 44.1 | 111.4 | | 1669 | Brand |
| Iron | Fe | 1539 | 2802 | 17.8 | Pre-Historic | |
| Silver | Ag | 960.5 | 1760.9 | 108.4 | Pre-Historic | |
| Arsenic | As | 814 | 1497 | 4.9 | 1250 | Albertus |
| Calcium | Ca | 850 | 1560 | 50.3 | 1808 | Davy |
| Tellurium | Te | 140 | 284 | | 1782 | Reichenstein |
| Selenium | Se | 220 | 428 | | 1818 | Berzelius |

34

# 9 Sheet and Strip Copper and Brass

John Winthrop is said to have been one of the first persons in America to put copper to use commercially. This was about 1664, at his small foundry in Lynn, Massachusetts. His earliest products made of copper were kettles, warming pans, candlesticks and ship sheathings. A while later, several different people made copper kettles in Philadelphia.

Paul Revere is credited with establishing the first copper rolling mill, at Canton, Massachusetts, in 1801. During the following year, mills at Waterbury, Connecticut, started rolling brass. As one would expect, operations at that time were conducted on a very small scale.

Today, in producing copper in the form of sheet and strip, a refinery cake of copper weighing 4000 pounds or more is delivered to a brass or copper mill. In the case of a copper base alloy suitable for hot rolling, such as one containing 70 per cent copper and 30 per cent zinc, the castings might weigh as much as 7000 pounds. Such a piece of metal would be approximately 26 inches wide by 136 inches long by 6¼ inches thick.

These cakes are placed in a muffle or furnace and brought to a red hot heat. While in this condition, the cakes of copper or brass are conveyed to breakdown rolls, where they are repeatedly passed back and forth, becoming thinner and longer with each successive rolling.

With most copper base alloys it is necessary to soften the metal between rolling operations. This is done by heating it in electrically or oil operated furnaces. The process is referred to as annealing.

Before further rolling, all imperfections are removed from both the top and bottom surfaces of the metal by milling

Bars of brass of an alloy of 70 per cent copper and 30 per cent zinc have been hot rolled and put through millers that have scalped or cut away the metal close to the surface on both sides.

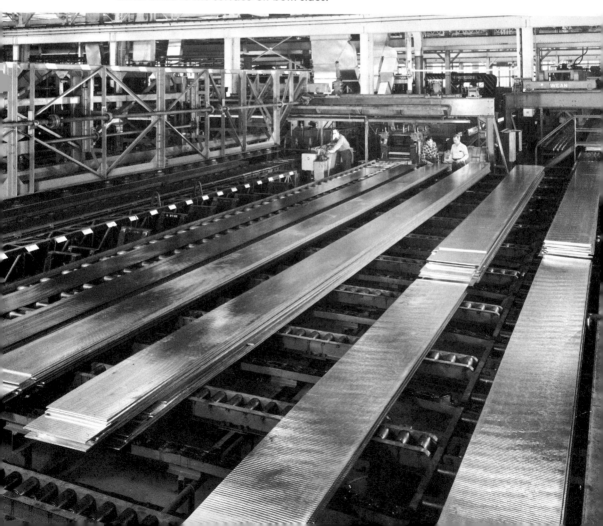

Rolling brass with a copper content of about 70 per cent on a 4-high mill

machines. The bars then go to what is referred to as a run-down mill where they are again rolled and further reduced in thickness to form ¼ to ⁵⁄₁₆ of an inch. When the metal emerges from this operation it is automatically coiled, annealed again to restore its softness, and rolled to specified gauges.

Plates, sheets and strips are supplied in various tempers or hardness. This is governed by the rolling that the metal alloy has received after the last annealing. The usual tempers are quarter-hard, half-hard, hard, extra-hard, spring and extra-spring. There are many instances, however, where metal is supplied fully annealed, referred to as soft.

# 10 Copper and Copper Base Alloy Tubes

## The Mannesmann Process

The Mannesmann method of producing tubes was developed years ago by two brothers of that name who lived in Mannheim, Germany. It is a quick and economical way of forming heavy-wall, seamless tubes, referred to as shells, from solid castings called billets. By this process, round billets, three inches in diameter and larger, are converted into tubes by rolling the red hot casting between two rolls, crowned in the center. The rolls squeeze the billet and produce a hollow condition at the center. The action of the rolls that grip and revolve the billet also forces it over a pointed rod, known as a mandrel. The function of this is to smooth the inside surface and control to a certain degree—the wall thickness.

The tubes are then pointed. Next, the pointed end is inserted through a die. This is a disc of hardened steel with a hole in it smaller than the tube, rod or wire which is to be reduced in size. Heavy jaws, connected to chains, powered by electrical motors, grip the pointed end of the tube and pull it through the die. The latter is held securely in a slot at one end

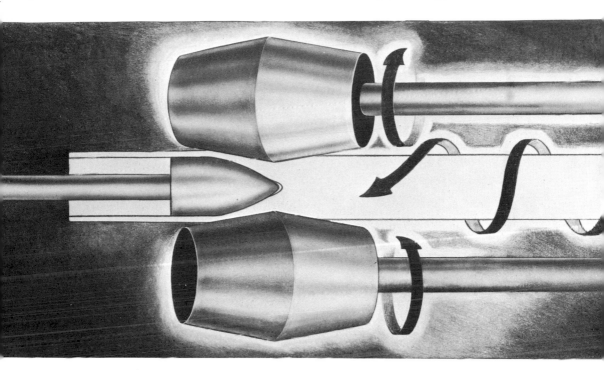

The principle of the Mannesmann process

Close view of a Mannesmann Machine

of the draw bench. In order to control accurately the inside diameter and the wall thickness of the tube, a highly polished machined steel cylinder two or three inches long that has been welded to a long steel rod of a smaller size, is threaded into the tube and held at the point where the tube comes in contact with the die. As the tube is drawn through the die it becomes smaller and the steel cylinder, known as a plug, over which the tube is drawn, not only serves to control the gauge but is a factor in maintaining a smooth or gun-barrel interior finish.

## Extrusion

A casting or billet five to 10 inches in diameter is sawed in pieces 8 to 10 inches in length and heated to a carefully controlled temperature beyond the point of being red hot. The billet is then inserted in a container of the press. Two concentric rams, or enormous plungers, operated by hydraulic pressures of several thousand pounds per square inch, then

The principle of tube drawing, which results in a thinning of the gauge, or walls, and a lengthening of the tube

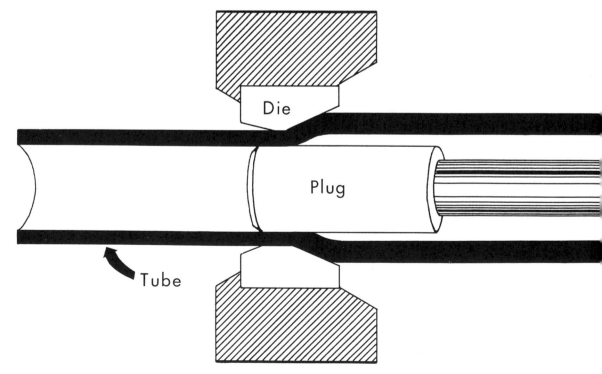

Die

Plug

Tube

Some of the many shapes of seamless tubes of copper and copper base alloys used in industry

come in contact with a dummy block placed between the rams and the billet. The dummy block is a heavy disc of steel with a hole in the center large enough to receive the inner or piercing ram. A slight pressure is applied to the outer ram, which has the effect of holding the billet, while the inner or piercing ram moves forward and punches out the center of the billet. The outer, or main ram, then forces the metal through the space between the inner ram and the die until the tube has been completely extruded.

When extruding shapes that are not hollow, a die of hard, heat resistant steel, with the shape to be extruded cut out of it, is placed ahead of a heated billet and pressure is applied to the latter. The hot metal, comprising the billet, is then forced through the shape opening in the die. By this extrusion method it is possible to manufacture hundreds of shapes in copper alloys which either could not be produced or would be too costly to make by any other process.

One of many examples would be a section in the shape of

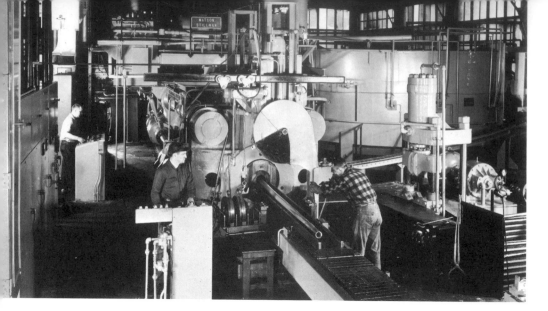

An extrusion press, showing a tube emerging. Such a press is capable of exerting a pressure of 2,500 pounds.

a gear. This could be extruded in a length twenty feet long, then cut in short pieces by a high speed saw. Many of the brass and bronze hand rails and parts of the ornamental work in some of the banks, apartment and office buildings that you have seen have been made from extruded sections of copper base alloys.

Diagram of extrusion process. *Upper left:* Showing billet in container. *Upper right:* Ram presses against the billet. *Lower left:* Mandrel punches the center out of billet. *Lower right:* Ram squeezes hot metal over mandrel and through die to form a rough tube.

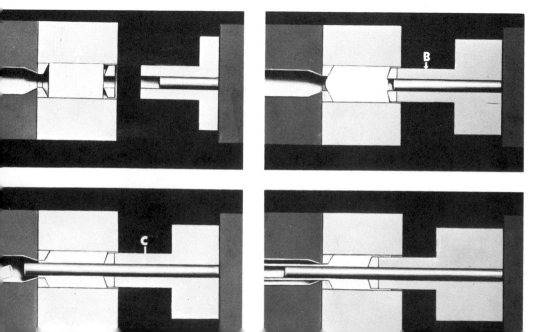

## Cast Shell Process

A rough casting of copper alloy metal is made in the form of a tube with thick walls. This is reduced in size by forcing it through dies. Then it is made even smaller by drawing on draw benches, previously described.

## Cupping Process

The usual method followed in making very large tubes is known as the cupping process. It consists of first rolling a casting or cake of copper or an alloy into a sheet, then cutting it into a circular shape. This piece of metal is then formed into a large cup, like a huge kettle on a powerful press. Successive operations reduce it in diameter and stretch it out. The closed end is then sawed off. Copper and copper bearing tubes have been made by this process as large as twenty-six inches in diameter.

## Impact Extrusion

In this method of manufacturing a very smooth and highly polished plunger of hard steel, operated by a powerful press, strikes a disc of copper or alloy with such force as to cause the cold metal to flow up the sides of the plunger and form a tube. This is known as impact extrusion. Tubes produced by such a process are limited to rather short lengths.

## Brazed Tubes

Copper base alloy tubes are sometimes made by brazing or welding. This process consists of strip metal being fed into an automatic machine which forms it into the shape of a tube and brazes or welds the joint in the next operation. The tube is then drawn through a die to smooth up the joint and to finish the product to accurate size and gauge.

Copper tubes that will be used for plumbing systems and hot and cold water lines, and for waste, vent and drainage work

### Tube Rolling

Briefly, the process of tube rolling consists of taking a tube which has been started either by the cast shell process or by extrusion and rolling it between two grooved rolls. The grooves are tapered both as to width and depth. As the rolls rock back and forth they reduce the size of the tube by what might be described as a kneading operation.

At the point where the grooved rolls come in contact with the tube, the latter is kept from collapsing by a steel plug which is fastened to the end of a rod that has been inserted into the tube and is held securely in place.

### Copper Tubes

As an example of the ductility of copper—meaning its ability to withstand stretching or forming without cracking

44

or breaking—seamless copper tubes have been made in sizes as small as 15/1000ths of an inch in diameter, with walls 3/1000ths of an inch thick.

A coil of copper 1/8th of an inch in diameter has been produced that was a mile long. Such a tube might have been used in the manufacture of certain delicate measuring or recording instruments, possibly in connection with the operation of an oil well.

Copper tubes of a certain diameter and wall thickness are trade marked with the manufacturer's name and the letters D, W, V. These letters stand for drainage, waste and vent, denoting where they are used in the plumbing industry. Tubes known in the trade as types K, L, and M, are used widely for hot and cold water lines in homes and in large buildings and for plumbing systems in industrial structures.

This is a view down one of the bays in a modern tube mill. The man at the left is operating a draw bench where tubes are being reduced in size and in wall thickness.

A section of the wire and rod department of a brass mill. Most of the product shown here will be sold to firms which will use it in the manufacture of hundreds of different items.

# 11 Copper and Brass Wire and Rod

Because copper is ductile it lends itself to drawing into extremely fine diameters. A bar of copper 3½ to 4 inches square by 4 or 5 feet long may be hot rolled and later drawn through a die made of a commercial diamond to the fineness of less than an ordinary hair, that is about three-thousandths of an inch. An ounce of such wire would be a mile long.

The dies used in drawing very fine wire are referred to as diamond dies for the reason they are made of an actual diamond, of commercial grade, through which a hole has been drilled. The diamond is then set or secured in the space drilled for it at the center of a disc of steel. A diamond is used for this because it is the hardest substance known and will not be worn away, as most steels would be by the action of the wire as it is drawn through the hole in the die. The size of the wire is so very fine that the least amount of wear requires a new die. If the latter were made of steel, it would mean a constant change of dies in order to draw a large volume of wire and still maintain a uniform size for the whole lot. On the other hand, many tons of the finest wire may be drawn through one diamond die before there is any evidence of wear. When the hole in the die finally does start to enlarge, the hole is polished or ground with diamond dust and made suitable for use in drawing wire of a slightly larger diameter.

While a large percentage of the amount of copper used annually goes into wire, rods, strips and drawn shapes for the electrical industry, the alloys of copper, in the form of wire and rod, supplied either in coils or straight lengths, account for a tremendous usage of the red metal. Hundreds of tons of brass rods and wire are used every year by many plants for the manufacture of brass and bronze screws and a great variety of small items for a thousand uses.

Millions of pounds of high strength copper base alloys are employed in articles used each year on the land and sea and in the air, wherever a combination of strength, weldability and resistance to corrosion are among the principal requirements.

Good examples are copper bearing welding rods. There are more than a dozen varieties of these copper alloy rods, each suited for a particular situation. By using the proper alloy, a light or heavy section of cracked or broken machinery may be repaired with a resulting strength at the weld of almost that of the original section. By welding together large sections of damaged iron and steel, weighing several tons, substantial savings have been made, not only by avoiding the cost of a whole new part, but also by lessening the length of time that an important producing machine is out of operation.

# 12 Copper and Communication

Thoroughly refined, high-conductivity copper is required in the production of wire and cable for electrical use. The process in a wire mill starts with a refinery shape that usually measures approximately 3½ inches by 5 inches by 54 inches long weighing about 250 pounds. This is known as a wire bar. It is heated to a temperature around 900 degrees Centigrade and passed through a series of grooved rolls from which it emerges in the form of a round rod one-quarter to three-eighths of an inch in diameter and over 500 feet long. During the heating it acquires an oxide scale which is removed by immersing it in an acid bath, a procedure known as pickling. After the elongated rod has been dipped in hot water to remove the acid, it is ready for drawing into wire.

Wire drawing is a cold-working process and the rod, which is in the form of a coil, is drawn through a series of smaller and smaller dies until the final diameter is reached. The dies are continuously lubricated by fluids which include a soapy mixture and special oils.

For electrical use, the bare copper wire is insulated by

covering it with plastic or a compound containing some rubber.

There are a great many types of cables such as telephone, power, lead covered, oil filled, gas filled, coaxial, submarine, to mention only a few.

The design of certain kinds of cables required a great deal of preliminary study, knowledge and research. This careful preparation also applies to the manufacturing procedure.

## Telegraph Cables

There are more than 7,500,000 miles of copper wire in the telegraph systems of the world. Over one-third of this is in the United States.

When you have sent a cable message to a friend in Europe, South America or some other country across one of the many vast oceans, have you ever given any thought as to how it managed to get there?

It went by copper cable. Today, there are millions of miles of copper wires under the seas of the world. These make up the thousands of miles of cable that connect various continents and islands on the globe in a great communication system.

It is possible to send telegraph messages over a cable at the rate of several hundred words a minute. It is interesting to note that the original Morse code, or system of signals for the sending and receiving of telegrams, is still used everywhere today. Samuel F. B. Morse's first underwater messages were sent by means of a copper wire laid in a section of New York Harbor.

The next submarine telegraphic development occurred in 1845, when Ezra Cornell, who later founded Cornell University, transmitted messages over a copper cable that ran through twelve miles of water.

The following year, Charles West, an Englishman, tried to lay a copper cable from England to France but lack of money forced him to abandon the project.

During the next few years more progress was made and, in 1850, Cyrus W. Field, an American businessman, and the Brett brothers of England were instrumental in forming a company to lay a telegraph cable between England and America. After numerous attempts and many failures, a successful cable was finally laid. Some of the transatlantic cables are at depths of over four miles below the surface of the sea.

In 1904, the first telegraph cable connecting Honolulu, Midway, Guam and Manila was completed, a distance of 9,600 miles.

Would there have been transatlantic cables if there had not been such a thing as copper? Who knows? But the fact

Here are 23 miles of submarine cable in one of the storage tanks at Western Electric Company. They will soon be deep in the Atlantic as part of the new telephone link.

that the red metal was available certainly speeded up the thinking that led to the idea of undersea communication and many other developments that have given us a better way of life.

## Telephone Cables

There are eighty million telephones in the United States, connected by 337 million miles of copper wire and cable, enough to circle the globe 13,500 times. All this has been accomplished since Alexander Graham Bell invented the telephone in 1876.

There are single telephone cables that are made up of more than 2500 individual insulated copper wires, each one of which carries hundreds of conversations into, out of and around New York City, each day. Telephone cables are made for direct burial in the ground. They are especially designed to withstand the corrosive action of various soils and, also, to resist ground hogs and other rodents which very frequently chew ordinary cable. Several thousand copper wires, each representing a telephone subscriber, are enclosed in a single cable with a copper sheath which is then covered by a tough plastic material.

One type of undersea or submarine telephone cable consists of a central conductor of solid copper wire wrapped with three copper tapes and then insulated by a thick covering of polyethylene plastic. To complete the electrical transmission path, six narrow copper tapes are laid over the plastic, one on top of the other. The next operation applies a wide overlapping copper tape to prevent marine borers from eating into the cables. Then a heavy layer of jute yarn is wound around the cable, serving as a cushion for the steel armor wires which are then wrapped around it for the purpose of strength. To provide for additional protection, the armor wires are covered

Cable Ship *Long Lines* at dockside, waiting to take on a cargo of copper submarine cable made by Western Electric Company

with two layers of impregnated jute. The outside diameter of such a cable is 1¼ inches.

Today, it is as easy and clear to talk by telephone with a person ten thousand miles away in another part of the world, far across the ocean, as it is to chat with a friend only a few blocks away.

At the beginning of 1963, the submarine telephone cables in operation were as follows:

The first was a short one from the United States to Cuba, completed in 1950. The first transatlantic telephone cable came into use in 1956. This stretched between the United States and the British Isles, via New York, Newfoundland, Scotland and then to England. During the same year, a tele-

Laying submarine telegraph cable in mid-ocean during a bad storm

phone cable was laid from the State of Washington to Alaska. The next one, which connected California with Hawaii, became operative in 1957. In 1959 another was laid between Newfoundland and France.

Others connect Florida and Puerto Rico, New Jersey and Bermuda, Florida and the Island of Jamaica. Between Puerto Rico and the United States the cable drops to a depth of five miles.

During the latter part of July 1963, the American Telephone and Telegraph Company's new 511-foot cable ship, *Long Lines*, started laying the western section of a 3500-mile cable which will be the first direct telephone link between the United States and England. The cable was made by Western Electric Company, at their Baltimore Works, and required a total of 12,250 tons of copper or 3½ tons per mile.

Sometime during 1964, another telephone cable will be laid between the west coast of the United States and Hawaii and then on to Japan. When entirely completed, this installation will be close to 11,000 miles long. Approximately 800 pounds of the highest grade of copper, known in the trade as OFHC (oxygen free high conductivity), will be used for each mile of this new type cable. This makes a total of 4400 short tons of the red metal for the completed project.

Overseas telephone service now links one hundred thirty-five countries and territories.

## Electric Power Lines

Another invaluable use for copper is in the manufacture of wire and cable for power lines to carry electricity for such essential purposes as heating, lighting, cooking, air conditioning and the operation of machinery. This use extends throughout rural areas in the illuminating of farmhouses, country schools, and the supplying of power to run everything from milking machines to television sets.

Of course, the greatest concentration is in the urban areas where there is a most intricate interweaving and overlapping of an amazing and highly efficient giant cobweb of wires and cables.

Most residents of New York City probably have no idea that there is what might be called a copper mine under them, fashioned by man in the form of wires and cables. Consolidated Edison Company of New York has over 326 million pounds of copper in its electrical system, 90 per cent of which is underground.

## Ship Radio

Copper also makes possible the complicated equipment that enables 1400 vessels to maintain radio telephone contact with transocean shore stations.

# 13 More of the Endless Uses of Copper

The distribution of the use of copper in the United States is approximately as follows: electrical equipment 19 per cent, light and power industry 18 per cent, building construction 16 per cent, industrial equipment 10 per cent, motor vehicles 9 per cent, communication 6 per cent, household appliances 3 per cent, railroad and marine 3 per cent, electronics 3 per cent, scientific equipment 2 per cent, military 6 per cent and miscellaneous 5 per cent.

During the year 1961, the use of new copper in the United States was at the rate of 15 pounds for every person in the country. This makes a total of 4,080,900,000 pounds or well over two million tons.

If we added the copper scrap used, the 1961 rate would be 22 to 23 pounds per person.

This is an important indicator of how much higher our standard of living is than some to be found in certain other areas of the globe.

In 1962, more than 414,000,000 pounds of copper tubes—not to mention the copper content in the valves, fittings and fixtures—were installed in the plumbing and heating systems of homes, hospitals, schools, hotels, office buildings and industrial structures throughout America. Copper was used because it will not rust, it is sanitary and it will last for years.

Over three million pounds of copper and copper base alloys were used for a long list of items, from propellers to ornamental trim, in the construction of the S. S. *United States* of the United States Lines Company, the world's fastest ocean liner. She is 990 feet long, has 12 decks, 18 elevators, accommodates 1,930 passengers and has a crew of over 1,000. She was designed by Gibbs & Cox and built by Newport News Shipbuilding & Dry Dock Company at a cost of eighty million dollars.

Approximately three million pounds of copper and its alloys were used by the John Brown Shipbuilding Company on the Clyde in the building of the 81,237 ton R. M. S. *Queen Mary* of the Cunard Lines.

The Capitol building in Washington, D. C., is protected by a copper roof.

Architects Miles Van der Rohe and Philip Johnson specified and used over 3½ million pounds of copper and its alloys

SS *United States* passing the skyscrapers of lower Manhattan, outward bound for Europe

in the construction of the thirty-eight story Seagram building, located at 375 Park Avenue, New York City, the world's first bronze skyscraper.

The buildings at the United States Naval Academy, at Annapolis, Maryland, are protected from rain, wind and the rugged salt air blowing off Chesapeake Bay by several hundred thousand pounds of copper, used for the roofs, flashings, gutters, ventilating system, etc.

Over 1,000,000 pounds of copper were used in building New York's Empire State Building.

Copper, 2,700,000 pounds of it, was also used in the construction of New York's Grand Central Terminal, undoubtedly the busiest railroad station in the world. This copper was in the form of sheets for the roof; wires and cables for lighting and communications; pipes, tubes, fittings, fixtures and valves for the plumbing, heating and air conditioning, also for such uses as electrical fixtures, ornamental work and hardware.

The Eddystone Division of Baldwin-Lima-Hamilton Corporation have made many propellers for some of the largest

The 38-story Seagram Building, world's first bronze skyscraper, located on Park Avenue in New York City. Several million pounds of copper were used in its construction.

Extruded bronze shape. The finished shape at the right was designed for the Seagram Building. It was furnished in varying lengths up to 26' 4" and weighing up to 275 pounds per length.

ships in service. Recently they produced one that was 24 feet, 8 inches in diameter. Most propellers are cast of manganese bronze, where copper is the base metal, combined with varying amounts of zinc, tin and manganese. Such a composition results in an alloy that will not rust. It is also very strong and will withstand the terrific wear to which such a piece of equipment is subjected.

The next time that you take a trip in a fishing boat, a cruiser or a yacht, you might find that the propeller shaft which transmits power from the engine to the bronze propeller is also bronze. One of the alloys in wide use for shafting is "Tobin Bronze," with a composition of: Copper 60 per cent, Zinc 39.25 per cent, Tin .75 per cent. This alloy, together with the time-tested way in which it is produced by rolling a cast billet, results in a tough, strong, corrosion resistant product that has become one of the standards in the marine industry, whether it be a pleasure craft or a commercial fisherman's boat operating out of Key West, New Orleans or Tampico, Mexico or Lima, Peru.

Thousands of tons of copper tubes are used in the production of the fifty-eight million tons of sugar which the peoples of the world consume each year. Nothing as satisfactory as copper has been found to take the place of the red metal in its ability to resist the heat and corrosive action of the cane juices during the extracting and refining processes.

The Pullman car that you ride in has 2,000 pounds of copper throughout its construction to insure efficient, safe and comfortable railroad transportation.

Over 50,000 pounds of copper and its alloys are used in the building of each one of the nuclear submarines for the United States Navy. This is further evidence that copper can be relied upon to give a good performance.

The super airliners of today, such as the Boeing 707, have 2,000 pounds of copper—most of which is in the form of wire —built into their complicated equipment.

Approximately 180,000 feet of copper wire is used in every Atlas missile, together with copper tubes, fittings and bearings with a high copper content.

In the years to come, we will hear a great deal about converting salt water to fresh water. There are presently several such units in operation in America and overseas. One hundred tons of copper and copper base alloys form a major part of some of the larger apparatus providing usable water to com-

Copper was the base metal used in casting this 38-ton propeller.

munities that would otherwise suffer for want of a safe and adequate supply.

There is an average of 25 to 35 pounds of copper in each of the 6,943,556 passenger automobiles and the 1,253,671 trucks manufactured in the United States in 1962.

It would be difficult to name an industry where copper is not used. If it is not an integral part of the finished item, it is employed as a vital segment of the equipment or machinery that is essential today.

## Copper and Coinage

As long ago as 20 B.C., the Romans were making coins of copper. However, the real art of coinage did not develop until 700 B.C. This was in the area of Lydia, in Western Asia Minor. From then until the middle of the nineteenth century, four metals—copper, gold, silver and iron, in varying combinations and proportions, formed the basis of the world's coinage system.

In 1850, the Swiss were responsible for revolutionizing the making of coins and added still more refinements in 1881. They developed a new coinage alloy containing 62 per cent copper, 23 per cent zinc and 15 per cent nickel.

These efforts of the Swiss stimulated other nations to experiment with new methods and alloys and, in 1857, the United States issued a one cent piece containing 88 per cent copper and 12 per cent nickel. Later, in 1860, Belgium followed with coins made up of 75 per cent copper and 25 per cent nickel. This alloy became the standard of many of the minor coinage systems of the world.

The standard silver dollar contains 90 per cent silver and 10 per cent copper.

There are 145 pennies in a pound and 290,000 in a short ton (2000 pounds).

The mints of the United States government use anywhere

The new Boeing 707-320B turbofan, with a payload range of over 6,000 miles, uses 2,000 pounds of copper, mostly wire, in its construction.

from 2000 to 7000 tons of copper each year for the minting of pennies. The latter account for three-fourths of the regular coins produced in the United States. A penny is now 95 per cent copper and 5 per cent zinc and tin. The addition of these other metals, particularly the tin, results in an alloy tougher than pure copper so the coin offers more resistance to wear.

Raw copper figures prominently in barter transactions in many areas of the world. Certain countries that have copper deposits but no smelting or refining facilities, Norway for example, have at times sent their copper ore to a company-owned refinery in Belgium. There it is refined and the service charge paid for by the refinery retaining some of the refined copper. At times, Chile has sent copper to Argentina in exchange for beef cattle. Coffee, salt fish, wool and ships have been traded for copper on numerous occasions and very likely will continue to be.

## Nickel Silver

Centuries ago, the Chinese knew nickel silver as "*Pack-fong.*" As far as is known, they were the first to mix nickel with copper to create an entirely new group of alloys that has since been broadened to include many combinations.

It was not until 1823 that two German scientists developed this class of alloys. At that time the metal was referred to in

Germany as deutsches silber. Later this became known in Europe and the United States as German silver and, since World War I it has been called nickel silver.

Several years ago in South America, particularly in Chile, Peru and Argentina, nickel silver was referred to as *Alpaca*. The only explanation my friends in those countries have been able to give me concerning the origin of the word *Alpaca* in connection with a copper base alloy containing nickel is the following:

"It is generally known that wool from the South American animal, the alpaca, is superior to sheep's wool and when they wanted a strong, nonrustable, durable metal with a silverlike color, and which had certain wearing qualities that were better than copper they called it *Alpaca*."

The probability is that the first *Alpaca* metal was a mixture of about 65 per cent copper, 18 per cent nickel and the balance zinc. Or it could have been one of the several alloys of copper and nickel known as cupro nickel.

Nickel silver is finding wide use in the field of electronics. A large percentage of the keys, for locks, that are used today are made of nickel silver to which a small amount of lead has been added to the alloy and still is employed in the manufacture of forks, spoons, trays and certain types of dishes which are plated with silver and sold as silver-plated ware.

Cupro nickel alloys contain only copper and nickel. One alloy in this group with a mixture of 70 per cent copper and 30 per cent nickel is a standard for the tubing, referred to as salt water lines, which convey corrosive salt water that is circulated throughout the fighting ships of the United States and the ships of other navies of the world. Because of its resistance to corrosion, a large volume of cupro nickel tubes is used in the condensers—essential equipment for the generation of power—in naval ships, ocean liners, refineries and power plants where water and other operating conditions are particularly severe.

# 14 Edison and a Cubic Foot of Copper

In September 1882, Thomas Alva Edison established the first generating plant for the transmission of electric power in the United States. This supplied energy for the lighting of some of the streets of New York City.

Four years earlier, by inventing and producing the first incandescent lamp, Edison had become responsible for putting copper into large scale practical use because of its exceptionally high efficiency as a conductor of electrical energy. There was a time when the many inventions of Edison accounted for one-quarter of the amount of copper used in the United States annually.

In this connection there is a story that illustrates the way Edison reasoned in regard to everything with which he had anything to do. Years ago, during that period when the inventions of Edison were consuming such a high percentage of the copper marketed in the United States, the presidents of four of the large copper mining companies paid a visit to Mr. Edison's plant at East Orange, New Jersey. They found Mr. Edison at work in old clothes, wearing a yellow sweater with many holes in it where acid had spattered on it. They announced that they had come to express their appreciation for what he had done for the copper industry and had decided to present him with a yacht.

He smiled and said, "That would be wonderful but I'm afraid I will always be too busy to ever find time to enjoy a yacht." After hesitating a moment, he continued, "Gentlemen, if you still want to give me something, I would much like to have a block of copper twelve inches square with the weight inscribed on it."

A twelve-inch cube of copper. Quite a contrast from a yacht! That would be easy, the gentlemen thought—until they talked to their metallurgists, back at their operations centers.

"A twelve-inch cube of copper should weigh exactly 558.14

Copper was one of the essential elements in the manufacture of this enormous rotor for a hydrogen cooled turbine generator that will supply electricity to thousands of homes.

pounds and Mr. Edison knows it," was the unanimous reply of the metallurgists. "And when we cast it, we are not certain whether or not we can eliminate some of the gases that will be formed and have it weigh precisely what it should weigh."

They made nine different castings, probably using a very small amount of phosphorous as a deoxidizer, to eliminate the gases and produce a sounder mass of metal. Each time they made some progress toward their desired goal, each cube weighing slightly more than the one before.

In spite of their efforts, the cube that finally went to Thomas Edison was several pounds short of the theoretical weight of 558.14 pounds. When it was delivered, Mr. Edison immediately looked at the inscribed weight.

"Wonderful!" he exclaimed. "You are a few pounds shy but several pounds closer to the weight that it should be than the last time it was tried by someone else."

One of Edison's close associates who told this story said, "Mr. Edison always had a good reason for everything that he did." Then he added, "Without mentioning the problem to the copper people, he wondered whether or not they knew about the casting difficulty and how close they would come to solving it."

There have been so many developments in metallurgy since then that, today, a twelve-inch cube of copper could undoubtedly be cast and have it weigh exactly what it should weigh.

# 15 Copper in Many Lands

From early morning until well after dark you will find Hasmuka, the genial tea seller, at his usual place on the streets of Kampur, India, dispensing tea from an ancient copper base alloy jar handed down from his father and grandfather.

His world is the busiest street in the area, crowded almost continuously with all manner of native people, water buffaloes, camels and rickshaws. He sells his tea in copper cups for a few copper coins or anas, which are worth less than a United States penny.

Across the street from him, three men are sitting on the parched earth. The sound of their crude hammers pounding on metal rises above the din around them. Each has a sheet of copper that once was known in the brass and copper mills in the United States as an India sheet. The trio are fashioning the red metal into water jugs or pots in which rice and other grains will be cooked for some of India's 437 million population.

One of the men has a long white beard and his lined and leathery forehead blends with the metal that he is fashioning. He learned how to do this work from his father who learned from his father before him.

High copper content bronze bells, weighing several tons, ready to be installed in St. George's Church, Erie, Pennsylvania

"It is an honorable trade," he says with a toss of his head, "and no one makes better copper trays or pots in Kampur than I."

Among the lower classes in India, a family's wealth is sometimes gauged by the number of brass and copper utensils it possesses. Durable copper receptacles are handed down from generation to generation there and in many areas of the Middle East as well.

India has several copper deposits but as of now it has only one important producing copper mine. This is located northwest of Calcutta. It does not take care of India's needs and, just now, that country requires an increasing amount of copper for many uses of which the conveying of electricity for its expanding industries is an example.

Turkey has copper mines and some of their output finds its way to the copper mill at Alexandria, Egypt, where copper sheets and circles are fashioned into pots and pans for cooking.

Japan, too, has copper mines but not nearly enough of the red metal for her constantly growing needs. Therefore, she is a steady customer for the producers in some countries, for either commercially pure copper or for concentrates for refining in Japan. After being refined it is manufactured into sheets, rods, wires or tubes by the brass mills and wire and cable plants of Japan.

Australia has several copper mines, one being located on the Island of Tasmania. In fact, there is hardly any country in the world where copper has not been found.

I have been in the ancient foundry in Naguib, located on a steep mountain to the north of Beirut, Lebanon. Naguib is known as the bell man and he belongs to the eighth generation of his family who, for many years, have designed and cast bells that have been shipped to the four corners of the earth. Most of Naguib's bells are two or three feet in diameter and weigh several hundred pounds.

"What alloy?" I asked Naguib. He smiled and talked about something else.

Without any doubt, copper is the base metal for his bells, with the right amount of zinc and lead added to make the mixture flow better—and some tin and possibly a little manganese included to strengthen it. At any rate, Naguib knows the secret of how to get a good casting and how to combine metals to produce delightful sounds.

"Shape is important too," he told me as he tapped a bell with his fingers, holding his watch so that I could see that, even with the slight touch that he had given it, it rang for a minute and a half.

"Come and see me again," he exclaimed cheerfully as he patted the bell on the floor beside him as if it were a child.

One of the greatest examples of statuary bronze is the colossal bronze Buddha at Kamakura, southwest of Yokohama, in Japan. It is six or more stories high, weighs several hundred tons and was erected sometime during the thirteenth century. The copper content is probably 80 to 85 per cent and we can only guess how it was possible to cast and erect such a gigantic mass of metal which is viewed with awe and admiration by thousands of Japanese and foreign travelers every year.

Another recent achievement in copper is the huge dome of the Academy of Science Building in Canberra, Australia. This unusual structure used twelve tons of copper.

Naturally, the use of copper plumbing is not confined to the United States. One of the many examples of the broadening use of copper for this purpose is to be found in Mexico today. Over 100,000 pounds of copper tubing in sizes one-half inch to twelve inches in diameter, together with tons of bronze fittings and valves, were used in Mexico City's tallest structure, the forty-three-story Latino-Americano Insurance Building whose sharp tower serves as a beacon for the increasing number of jets that zoom in and out of the picturesque airport nearby every day.

Twelve tons of copper were used in the construction of the dome of the unusual Academy of Science Building, in Canberra, Australia.

# 16 Copper Feathers

In several of the countries of Africa there is a bird known as the turaco or turako. There are a dozen or more species, ranging in size from fourteen inches to two and one-half feet tall.

Their soft plumage is gay, with green, blue and red predominating. Their tails are long, their heads topped with a large crest.

The matter which colors the red feathers of the turaco bird dissolves in water just like an inferior dye. Strange as it may seem, there is copper in this red pigment and no one has discovered from where it comes. The substance is well established and recorded by science as "turacin."

It was thought at first that the copper pigment resulted from the birds eating small grains of copper or copper bearing malachite ore. This theory was discarded when it was established that these strange and interesting birds are among the species which never feed on the ground. Instead, they get their food while in lofty trees, their diet consisting of fruit and certain types of bugs.

In an attempt to solve the baffling mystery, several turacos were captured alive. Apparently during the trapping procedure the fluttering of the birds' wings dislodged the red pigment on the feathers. However, after being kept in captivity for only a short while the pigment containing copper appeared on certain feathers coloring them red. Rain washed the pigment away but soon it reappeared.

The red feathers of the turaco of Africa still remain a mystery to ornithologists. The secret of this bird is interesting to consider but the solving of it wouldn't add a pound of copper for actual use.

The forty-three story Latin American Insurance Building, Mexico's tallest structure, where 100,000 pounds of copper tube and thousands of bronze fittings and valves were used for the plumbing installation

# 17 Copper in Agriculture and in Health

## Copper in Agriculture

The use of copper sulphate, mixed with many types of commercial fertilizers, has greatly increased the production of various crops such as tomatoes, potatoes and grapes. Experiments conducted over thirty years ago showed that copper sulphate gave certain soils an element that was an aid to the growth of an additional number of crops. By the use of copper sulphate, higher quality onions and lettuce are now grown in sections of New York State than had previously been possible. When added to the peat soils of the Everglades of Florida, it speeded the growth of over fifty different kinds of vegetables and grains in that area.

In the case of carrots, lettuce, onions and spinach, there is a noticeable improvement in their color when copper sulphate is used in the soil. For example, onions of the type that might ordinarily be yellow have become the wanted brownish-yellow instead of the not so desirable yellowish-green through the use of copper sulphate. Dull and faded green spinach and lettuce become a bright and vigorous green by the addition of some copper sulphate to the soil in which they grow. Often the flavor is also improved. This is very apparent in carrots and beets.

Experts in the science of soil chemistry agree that copper is a normal ingredient of almost all types of soil, although the amount varies considerably according to location.

## Copper and Health

It has long been known that copper is definitely essential to good health and is important in animal and human growth.

Copper occurs in foods, the amount varying widely from the larger content that is contained in fresh calf's liver to the much smaller amount in fresh celery. Such foods as oysters, chocolate, cocoa and molasses have an exceptionally high copper content.

Much time and attention has been devoted to the study of experimentation with copper and its effect on the health of human beings and animals and the following quotation is taken from the findings of authorities in the field.

Copper is not poisonous. Small amounts of copper do not accumulate in the body but are eliminated naturally.

Copper is found in nearly all soils and plants and in the vital organs and blood of virtually all animals and human beings.

It is essential to the good health and proper functioning of all plant and animal life and, when copper is lacking in plants, animals or humans, it must be supplied.

Copper is one of the necessary elements of life.

74

# 18  Copper in the Future

Everyone should be getting ready to live in the future because that is where all of us are going to spend the rest of our lives.

It seems certain that copper, the 8000-year old metal, is assured of an important place in the future as well as the past because of its outstanding qualities. Recently, a forging of pure copper weighing 5½ tons, one of the largest ever produced, was made at Worcester, Massachusetts, on a 50,000 ton forging press. It became a vital part of one of the largest United States missiles. Tons of copper wires and cables are being used constantly in the construction of missiles and the equipment that is necessary to fire them.

The great utility companies of the United States are using copper base alloy condenser tubes in their existing plants, as they have done for many years. Copper alloys are expected to play a still more important part in the construction and successful operation of the tremendous new power projects that are now in the planning stages.

Ocean liners and ships of the United States Navy use large quantities of copper alloy condenser tubes that are essential in the generating of the power necessary to drive these "greyhounds of the sea" through the water at the speeds that are

A section of the copper plumbing system in a modern skyscraper

required today. The size of such vessels and their speeds will surely be greater in the future and copper will play a part in these developments.

Records show that the United States petroleum demand is more than nine million barrels a day. Whether they be in this country, the Middle East or Venezuela or on the Islands of Curacao and Aruba in the West Indies, where Shell Oil and Standard Oil of New Jersey have extensive operations, it seems likely that the refineries of the world will continue to use copper base alloy condenser tubes as an essential part of their equipment.

As previously mentioned, nothing better than copper has been found for the tubes in the evaporators required for converting the juice of sugar cane into the many million tons of sugar produced in the world every year.

Since copper is the best commercial conductor of electricity, it will continue to play a major part in the design, construc-

76

tion and operation of the new and spectacular developments by the leading manufacturers of electrical apparatus.

The demand for new telephones is increasing at the rate of three million each year. The two million or more new homes built each year in the United States need plumbing, wiring and numerous electrical appliances where copper is the necessary element.

Newly developed protective coatings that will preserve the color of copper and its many alloys will stimulate its use in architecture and in other areas where appearance is of prime importance.

On the other hand, many of the buildings in America and in Europe are outstanding because of their roofs, spires and domes fashioned of copper that over the years have acquired a soft green patina.

Beryllium copper, which is copper with 1½ per cent to 2¼ per cent beryllium, could well find expanded uses. It has the quality of being heat treatable, meaning that, when heated to certain temperatures and cooled quickly by plunging it into water or oil, it hardens.

Fittings made from copper tubes are used for connecting plumbing, air-conditioning and refrigeration systems.

Copper played an important part in the construction of this generator assembly which will provide power for many factories.

The uses for boron copper could also show a substantial increase. This is an alloy of 99.98 per cent copper and .02 per cent boron. It is highly suitable for glass-to-copper seals in the manufacture of radio and television vacuum tubes and other electrical apparatus.

Other metals, such as cadmium, chromium, silicon, tellurium, and zirconium, have been alloyed with copper to produce metals with qualities that have found important uses in industry.

The fact that copper is such an agreeable mixer makes a countless number of combinations possible. Copper producers and brass and copper mills are devoting a great deal of time, effort and money to research and it seems certain that the large family of copper alloys will soon be much larger.

Copper fits firmly into our fast moving age of electronics and nuclear achievements and will surely continue to be one of the most important metals in the development of many things to come that will further our standard of living.

No metal has had a more distinguished past or can look forward to a brighter future than copper.

# INDEX

79

## EDWARD B. TRACY

was born on a farm in South Waterbury, Connecticut, in an area then known as the "Horse Pasture District." He attended public schools and later graduated from the Gunnery School, Washington, Connecticut, and Pratt Institute, Brooklyn, New York.

For several years he worked as a caster, then as a foreman in the rolling and wire mills of one of the large brass mills, and later became salesman and assistant manager of one of the plants of the same company. His subsequent positions were as manager of sales of certain special products, export manager and general sales manager. He is now Assistant to the Vice President in charge of sales.

In his travels as export manager, Edward Tracy has visited sixty countries, many of them several times. His home is in Washington, Connecticut.

He is active in the affairs of The Boys' Clubs of America and in those of his Alma Mater, the Gunnery School, a boarding school for boys that has been in existence for over a hundred years. He has been chairman of its board of trustees for several years.

Edward Tracy is interested in the outdoors and has had several articles on hunting, fishing and wild life published in several nationally known magazines. He has written five books for younger readers.